The Fabulous Adventures of Nasruddin Hoja

Ta-Ha Publishers Ltd.
1 Wynne Road,
London SW9 0BB
UK

Copyright © Ta-Ha Publishing Ltd.

Published Sha'ban 1422/November 2001 by:
Ta-Ha Publishers Ltd.
1 Wynne Road
London SW9 OBB
Website: http://www.taha.co.uk
Email: sales@taha.co.uk

General Editor: Afsar Siddiqui
Edited by: Abdassamad Clarke

British Library Cataloguing in Publication Data
Fabulous Adventures of Nasruddin Hoja, The
I. Title

ISBN 1 84200 031 4

Typeset by: Bookwright
Website: http://www.bogvaerker.dk/Bookwright
Email: bookwright@bogvaerker.dk

Printed and bound by: Deluxe Printers, London.

Contents

The Fabulous Adventures of Nasruddin Hoja

Introduction

There are several Nasruddin Hojas and that can be confusing. The Arabs call him Joha, the Turks know him as Nasruddin Hoja and the people of India, Pakistan and Iran as Mulla Nasruddin. But it is even more confusing than that. 'Hoja' or 'Khoja' and 'Mulla' all mean an 'imam', but this is no ordinary imam. This imam is three people.

The first is a fool. He is a complete idiot. The second is a rogue, somebody who is completely dishonest. The third sometimes looks like a rogue or an idiot or both, but is really quite wise. Do you think you can spot which is which?

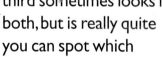
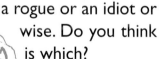

The next village

Nasruddin Hoja was standing in afield when a passer-by quizzed him, asking what the people in the next village down the road were like.

'Well, what did you think of the people in our village?' he asked the stranger.

'Block-headed, lazy, stupid and rude, if you must know,' replied the traveller.

'That's probably how you'll find them in the next village, too,' said the Hoja.

A little later, another passing stranger struck up a conversation with Nasruddin Hoja. He too asked what the people in the next village were like.

'How did you find the people in this village?' countered the Hoja again.

'Warm-hearted, smiling, gentle and hospitable,' answered the stranger.

'Then that's how you'll find them in the next village, too.'

Whom do you believe?

One day a friend visited the Hoja and said, 'Nasruddin, I want to borrow your donkey.'

'I'm sorry,' replied Nasruddin, 'but I've already lent it to someone else.'

As soon as he said this, the donkey brayed.

'But Hoja, I can hear the donkey! It's in the stable!'

Nasruddin told him with dignity, 'A man who believes the word of a donkey above my own, doesn't deserve to be lent anything!'

Then he shut the door in this friend's face,

The goat

Some people asked the Hoja once, 'What is your sun sign?'

He answered, 'The Goat.'

'What? There isn't any sign of the Zodiac called "The Goat."'

He said, 'But when I was born they told my mother that I was a "Capricorn".'

'Well, there you are then,' said one of the men to the Hoja.

The Hoja turned to him and said, 'But now I am forty years old. Can't a Capricorn grow up to be a goat in that time?'

3

I don't need your advice

One day the Hoja went to see a rich friend and said to him, 'Please give me some money.'

'But why?' asked the man.

'Well, I want to buy an elephant!' replied the Hoja.

'If you have no money, how can you afford to keep an elephant?' his confused friend asked.

'I came here to get money, not advice!' replied the Hoja.

Why I use a light

'I can see in the dark,' boasted the Hoja one day while sitting in a tea shop.

'If that's true,' said his friends, 'why do we sometimes see you carrying a light at night?'

'You see,' he replied, 'I only use a light to prevent other people from bumping into me.'

What's the use?

One day, the Hoja sat in the mosque to teach a class.

'O true believers, do you know what I am going to talk to you about today?' he asked.

'We have no idea,' they answered him in surprise, looking at each other.

'Well, if you have no idea at all, then what's the use of my talking to you?' he asked in indignation.

With that remark he left the mosque and went home.

The next week he returned to the mosque and once again sat to teach. He began: 'O believers, do you know what I am going to talk to about today?' he asked again.

'Yes,' answered the clever ones, who thought they had learnt from the mistake they had made the previous week.

'Well, if you already know then what's the use of my telling you?' he said. Again he left the mosque and went home.

The following week, he again entered the mosque, sat in his circle of students and asked the same question:

'O believers, do you know what I'm going to talk to you about today?'

The congregation had prepared their answer in advance: 'Some of us do and some of us don't,' they answered.

'In that case,' the Hoja said, 'let those who know tell those who don't.'

And he went home again,

The loan

One day a friend asked the Hoja for a loan, saying that he would repay him the following week. Nasruddin didn't believe him but he gave him the money anyway.

Much to his surprise, the man kept his word and repaid the loan.

A few months later, the same man wanted another loan from the Hoja and said to him, 'You know that my credit is good. Last time I repaid you promptly.'

'You're not going to get any money this time,' said the Hoja. 'You deceived me last time by repaying me when I thought that you wouldn't. I'm not going to let you deceive me again.'

At the police station

One day someone stole the Hoja's donkey so he immediately went to the Police Station and reported the theft. The Chief of Police said:

'Now Hoja, tell us. We'll do all we can to get your donkey back. After all, you are rather famous. Now please, start at the beginning and tell me exactly how it happened.'

The Hoja replied, 'Well, since I wasn't there when it happened, how am I supposed to know?'

What must be

A farmer came to the Hoja and asked him if his olive trees would bear that year.

'Of course they will,' replied the Hoja.

'Are you sure?' asked the farmer.

'Yes, I'm positive,' Nasruddin said.

A little later he took his donkey along the seashore looking for driftwood. He looked for hours but yet he found nothing. He headed for home tired and worn out. The same farmer saw him returning empty-handed and said:

'Hoja, you are a very wise man. You know that my olive trees will bear fruit and yet you didn't know that there wasn't any wood on the seashore. Why is this so?'

The Hoja replied, 'I know what must be, but I don't know what might be!'

I am a stranger here

Once, the Hoja visited a village not far from his town. As he was walking through the village a man asked him:

'Sir, what day is it today?'

The Hoja replied, 'I am a stranger here, you must ask one of the locals.'

I'm using it

The Hoja's neighbour wanted to borrow his clothes-line but the Hoja said, 'Sorry, but I'm using it. I'm drying flour on it.'

'How in the world can you dry flour on a clothes-line?' asked the neighbour.

'Well, It's not so difficult when you don't want to lend it out!' he answered.

At the mill

Once the Hoja went into a nearby mill and began to take handfuls of grain out of the sacks and put them into his own.

The miller came in and demanded, 'What are you doing there?'

'I am a fool,' quipped the Hoja. 'I just have to do whatever comes into my mind!'

'Well, how is it that it never came into your mind to take wheat out of your sack and put it into mine?' the mill-owner asked.

'Sir,' he replied, 'I am just a normal fool. I am not an absolute idiot!'

Sunlight

A neighbour came to the Hoja once and complained that there was no sunlight in his house.

The Hoja asked him, 'Is there any sunlight In your garden?'

'Yes, of course,' replied the man.

'Then move your house into your garden!' said the Hoja.

Congratulations

'Congratulate me!' exclaimed the Hoja to a friend. 'I'm a father now!'

'Well, congratulations!' replied his friend. 'Is it a boy or a girl?'

'Yes! But how did you know?' asked the Hoja.

Three monks

Once three learned Christian monks ware travelling through Turkey in the hope of disputing with the wisest man there. They asked the Sultan who this could he and he referred them to Nasruddin Hoja of Aksehir. The monks explained that they were interested in meeting him because they each had a question to ask him. So the Sultan summoned Hoja who came to the palace at once.

'Let them ask their questions,' Hoja said confidently, when the reason for the monks' visit was explained.

The first monk stepped up and asked, 'Sir, where Is the centre of the earth?'

'At this very moment that point is exactly under the right foot of my donkey,' he told them assuredly.

'How ca n you prove that?' asked the monk.

'If you don't believe me, measure the earth and you'll see,' Hoja answered.

The first monk left and the second stepped up and asked, 'How many stars are there in the sky?'

'As many as there are hairs on my donkey,' he replied.

'How can you prove that?' asked the monk.

'If you don't believe me, just count them,' he answered.

'How can one count all the hairs on a donkey?' protested the monk.

'As easily as one can count all the stars in the sky,' answered Hoja wisely.

The second monk stepped back in bewildered amazement and the third stepped up:

'How many hairs have I got in my beard?' he asked.

'As many as my donkey has in its tail,' replied Hoja.

'How con you prove that?' he asked.

'That's easy,' he replied confidently,'we can simply pluck the hairs out of your beard and my donkey's tail one by one and in this way we can easily count them!'

The third monk wasn't at all keen on this idea and he also withdrew somewhat in a state of shock. All three monks agreed that they were defeated and they were all converted to Islam.

He never goes back on his word

One of his friends asked Hoja, 'How old are you?'

'Forty,' he replied.

'But you said the same thing when I asked you that three years ago!' objected the friend in confusion.

'Yes,' replied Hoja, 'I never go back on my word!'

Duck soup

Hoja was passing by a lake one day when he saw a large number of ducks swimming in it. He was very hungry so he decided to catch one and have it for lunch. Hoja quietly tiptoed towards them and then dived to catch one. But to his disappointment they all flew away and he was left there wet and hungry. Then he sat down by the side of the lake, dipped a piece of bread into the water and began eating it.

A friend passed by, 'Good afternoon, Hoja,' he said, 'what are you eating?'

'Duck soup,' he replied.

The death of his donkey

One day Hoja was brokenhearted over the loss of his dear wife. All of his neighbours and friends tried to console and comfort him by saying, 'Don't worry about her, Hoja, we'll help you to find an even better wife!'

A short while later his donkey also died, but Hoja seemed to mourn even more over its loss than over the loss of his wife. Some of his friends noticed this and so they approached and asked him concerning this matter.

He replied, 'When my wife passed away, all my friends promised me that they would find an even better one for me, but so far no one has offered to replace my donkey!'

Child discipline

One day Nasruddin Hoja told his son to go and fetch some water from the well. He told him not to break the pitcher and then he proceeded to give him a hard spanking.

'Hoja,' asked a spectator, 'why do you spank your son when he hasn't done anything wrong?'

'Because it would be too late to punish him after he broke the pot, wouldn't it?' Hoja replied.

The moon in the well

One night Hoja was walking by a well when he had a sudden impulse to look inside of it. To his amazement he saw the reflection of the moon in the water

He exclaimed, 'The moon has fallen into the well! I must save it somehow!'

He looked around and found a rope with a hook on the end of it. So he threw it in the water and shouted, 'Grab the hook, moon, and hold tight! I'll pull you out.'

The rope latched onto a rock inside the well and Hoja pulled as hard as he could. Suddenly the hook broke free from the rock and Nasruddin fell over on his back. Lying there, he noticed the moon high up in the sky above. He heaved a sigh of relief and said, 'Well, it wasn't easy, but it's a wonderful feeling to know that I've delivered the moon from the well.'

The opposite

Someone asked Hoja once, 'Where is your nose?'

In answer to this question Nasruddin pointed to the back of his neck.

He started laughing at him and making fun of him saying, 'Hoja doesn't even know his front from his back!'

Hoja quickly responded, 'Well, if you don't know the back of something, how can you know it's front?'

No tail

Hoja was taking his mule to sell in the market one day when he noticed that its tail was dirty and tangled. He cut it off and put it in his bag.

Hours passed and no one was interested in buying his mule. Finally a prospective customer came up and began to examine the mule. Then he noticed that it didn't have a tail.

He exclaimed, 'What kind of a mule is this? It doesn't even have a tail!'

Hoja replied, 'Wait a minute! Let's talk about the price. The tail is not far away.'

To think of soup

One day Hoja was very hungry.

'If I just had a nice hot bowl of soup,' he thought, 'I would be so content.'

Just then someone knocked at the door. He opened it and there stood a young boy with an empty bowl in his hands.

The boy said, 'My mother is not feeling well. Can you please give her a little hot soup?'

'Oh, no!' exclaimed Hoja. 'Not even my thoughts are my own. I only have to think of soup and my neighbours can smell it.'

A generous tip

One day Nasruddin Hoja went to a Turkish bath. Since he was poorly dressed the attendants treated him poorly, giving him only at small piece of soap and a torn towel.

When he had finished, Hoja gave the workers a gold coin each. They wore amazed because Hoja had not complained about their treatment, but rather had given them a very large tip. Could it be, they wondered, that if they had treated him better he would have given them an even better tip?

One week later, Hoja came to the bath again, but this time the attendants treated him like a king. After being massaged, perfumed and treated with the utmost deference, he gave each worker a small copper coin, of very little value.

They both looked very disappointed, but Hoja said to them knowingly, 'These copper coins are for last time, the gold coins were for this time.'

I have the recipe

One day Hoja went to the market and bought a fine piece of meat: lamb liver. On the way home he met a friend who asked him how he was going to cook it.

He replied, 'I'm just going to fry it.'

'But I know of an excellent recipe for liver,' said the man, 'much better than simply frying it.'

So his friend wrote out the recipe for Hoja on a piece of paper and gave it to him.

Hoja has very pleased and excited about this delicious new recipe and he could hardly wait to get home to try it. Just before he arrived home, however, a large crow swooped down and grabbed the meat right out of his hands and flew away with it.

Hoja shouted at the crow angrily, 'But you're not going to enjoy it, you lousy thief! I've got the recipe here!'

The wind did it

Nasruddin Hoja climbed over a fence into someone's garden and started filling his sack with everything on which he could get his hands.

The gardener saw him and shouted, 'Hey, what are you doing here?'

'I was blown here by a strong wind,' said Nasruddin.

'And who uprooted the vegetables then?' asked the gardener.

'I was holding onto them to stop myself from being swept along by the wind,' answered Hoja.

'But then how is it that there are vegetables in your sack?' asked the gardener.

'That's funny,' Nasruddin replied, looking puzzled. 'I was wondering about the same thing when you came along!'

A fool

Once Hoja was carrying a large box of fragile glassware. Then he tripped and dropped it in the street and everything was completely shattered.

A crowd gathered round.

'What's the matter with you, idiots?' screamed Hoja. 'Haven't you ever seen a fool before?'

Playing the lute

One day Hoja's friends handed him a lute and asked him to play a song. Hoja was not musically inclined but nevertheless took the instrument in his hands and proceeded to strum the quill back and forth across the strings. It sounded terrible!

'Is that how to play a lute?' complained his friends. 'We've noticed that lute players find the note they want by moving the fingers of their left hand up and down the neck.'

'I'm not looking for any notes,' replied Hoja, 'I've already found them.'

It is better to ride backwards

One day while on the way to Aksehir with some friends, Hoja was riding on his donkey backwards. They thought that it was odd and so they asked him, 'Hoja, why are you riding the donkey backwards?'

He replied, 'If I ride the donkey the right way and go ahead of you, then you'd be offended. If you go ahead of me then that wouldn't be nice either. So then it's better to ride the donkey backwards like this and to be face to face with you!'

Shopping

Hoja went to the bazaar one day to buy some clothes. He picked out a fine-looking pair of trousers and the salesman packaged them for him. Just then, Hoja changed his mind and decided that he would rather have a light cloak.

'Give me a cloak instead,' he told the salesman.

After he chose a fine cloak the salesman wrapped it and gave it to him.

He was walking off with it when the man called after him, 'Sir, you haven't paid for the cloak yet!'

'But I left you the trousers for it,' explained Hoja.

'But you didn't pay for the trousers either!' the salesman exclaimed in astonishment.

'Of course not!' Hoja replied in exasperation. 'Why should I pay for trousers that I didn't take?'

They all taste the same.

Hoja loaded his donkey with two baskets full of grapes that he had picked from his garden and set off for the market to sell them. On the way he met a group of small children who shouted for joy when they saw all the grapes.

'Mister,' they all cried, 'please give us some grapes.'

Hoja saw that there were twelve children and figured that he would lose money if he gave each of them one. So he broke off a stalk with only six on it and gave it to one of the boys.

'Mister, is that all you can give us?' complained the children.

Hoja replied, 'Listen! All these grapes taste the same, so it makes no difference whether you eat half of one or a bunch of them!'

A vicious dog

Once Hoja was passing by a cemetery when he saw a dog digging around a grave. So he lifted up his cane to strike at it when the dog suddenly bared its teeth and jumped towards him with an angry snarl.

Hoja jumped back quickly and with a forced smile said, 'Down boy! Sorry for bothering you. Go on about your business!'

The wedding invitation

Hoja saw that a wedding was being celebrated in a nearby house and wished that he could be there. He had an idea. He folded a piece of paper, put it in an envelope, knocked on the door and said, 'Here, my friend, is my invitation to your wedding celebration.'

Then he boldly entered the house and sat down at the table and began to partake of all the delicious delicacies that were prepared.

The host opened the envelope, took out the letter and said, 'This paper is blank! There is nothing written on it!'

'I was in a hurry,' explained Hoja, 'and your servant didn't have time to write out the invitation.'

Whom do you love the most?

At one time Hoja had two wives. People wanted to know which he loved the most.

They asked him, 'If you were in a boat with both your wives, which one would you save first if it capsized?'

Hoja turned to his first wife and asked, 'Dear, you know how to swim, don't you?'

Ladder for sale

One day Hoja scaled a wall and pulled his ladder over into the garden on the other side. The owner caught him in his garden and shouted at him, 'Hey! What are you doing here?'

'Well, I… am selling this ladder,' improvised Hoja.

'Fool,' replied the owner of the land, 'you can't sell a ladder in a garden!'

'Ah, it is you who are a fool!' He wisely replied. 'For you don't know that a ladder can be sold absolutely anywhere.'

A learned man

A farmer once brought Hoja a letter and asked him to read it to him. 'The handwriting is so bad that I can't read it,' he said.

The man became angry and said, 'You wear the turban of a learned man and you can't even read a letter!'

Hoja took off his turban and placed it before him. He said, 'If you think that everyone who wears a turban is a learned man, then you put it on and see if you can read it.'

A wonderful thought

One day Hoja asked his wife to make some halwa, a very delicious sweet made from sesame seeds, honey, and other ingredients. She made quite a lot and Hoja ate nearly all of it.

That night in bed he woke her up and said, 'I've just had a wonderful thought.'

'What is it?' asked his wife curiously.

'Bring me the rest of the halwa and I'll tell you,' he said.

She got up and brought him the halwa and when he had finished eating it, she said, 'Now I won't be able to go back to sleep until you tell me your thought.'

'The thought, said Hoja, 'was this: Never go to sleep without finishing the halwa that has been made that day.'

If I was on it

One day Hoja lost his donkey. While looking for it he was also rejoicing. When the people saw him they couldn't understand why he was so happy, and they wanted to find out the reason for this.

Hoja told them, 'I'm happy because I wasn't riding the donkey when it got lost. If I had been, I'd be lost now too.'

Old vinegar

Hoja's friend came up to him one day and asked, 'I heard that you have some vinegar that is forty years old. Can I have some?'

'Certainly not!' he replied. 'If I had kept giving it away it wouldn't be forty years old now.'

Well, I was in it

One day his neighbours asked Hoja, 'We heard some noises in your house last night and we were wondering what had happened?'

Hoja told them, 'My cloak fell down the stairs.'

They replied, 'But Nasruddin Hoja, a cloak is just tailored out of cloth, and it couldn't have made that much noise.'

Hoja said impatiently, 'Well. I was in it at the time.'

I can't tell the difference.

Late one night Hoja was asleep in bed with his wife when she woke him up and said, 'Dear, I need to go to the bathroom. I left the candle on the right side of the bed. Can you please hand it to me so that I can light it?'

Hoja replied, 'How do you expect me to tell my right hand from my left in the dark?'

In the barber's shop

Hoja went to a clumsy barber one day who started to shave him with a blunt razor. Every time he nicked him the barber would dab a small piece of cotton on the cut to stop the bleeding. When he got done with one side of Hoja's face, it was covered with many small dabs of cotton.

As the barber was about to shave his other cheek, Hoja looked at himself in the mirror and suddenly jumped up and said, 'That's enough, thank you, my friend! Now that I have cotton on one side of my face, I have decided to grow barley on the other.'

A gossip

One day a man came up to Hoja while he was sitting in a tea shop and began to gossip on all kinds of private affairs. Hoja couldn't understand why this stranger was telling him all these thing. He interrupted him by saying, 'Excuse me, but I don't even know you; why then are you telling me all these things?'

'Oh no!' replied the man. 'I noticed that your turban is the same as mine and so is your cloak, so I thought you were me.'

The coffin is coming

One of the men of Aksehir died.

His wife was heartbroken over the loss of her loved one. She cried and lamented, 'Oh, my husband, where have you gone? To a place where there is no fight, no food, nothing!'

When Hoja heard this, he ran home and told his wife, 'Hurry! Get ready! The coffin is coming to our house.'

Salty milk

Hoja and his friend were thirsty, so they stopped at a cafe for a drink. They decided to share a glass of milk because they had only a little money. Then his friend said to him, 'You drink your half first. I have some sugar here but it is only enough for me, enough for half a glass of milk.

'Add it now,' said Hoja, 'so that my half will be sweetened too.'

'Definitely not!' replied his friend. 'I like my milk sweet and I've only got enough sugar for me.'

Hoja happened to have some salt in his bag so he said to his friend, 'All right, I'll drink my half first, but I like my milk salty.'

Are we moving?

Late one night a thief broke into Hoja's house and began to stuff everything movable into his sack. Nasruddin Hoja was awakened by all the noise and he came downstairs and saw the man. Then he began to help the burglar fill his sack. The thief was dumbfounded.

He exclaimed, 'Sir, what are you doing? Why are you filling my sack?'

'Oh, I thought we were moving,' Hoja replied.

They have stopped fighting

At midnight Hoja heard a lot of commotion outside his window. He wrapped his blanket around himself and went outside to see what was happening.

He saw two men fighting and he asked them why, and tried to break it up.

Without answering, one of them ripped the blanket off Hoja and both of them quickly ran away. So poor Hoja ashamedly walked back into his house naked and returned to his bed.

'What was all the fighting about?' asked his wife.

'It was over our blanket,' he said. 'Now that they have got it they have stopped fighting.'

It is not mine

One day Hoja was eating a delicious piece of lamb, when a boy came up to him and asked for some.

Nasruddin Hoja answered, 'I cannot give you any because it is not my meat, it's my wife's.'

'Then why are you eating it?' he asked.

'I have to eat it,' he said. 'My wife told me to.'

A dream

One hot summers day, Hoja was taking a nap on the porch. He dreamt that a complete stranger promised to give him ten pieces of gold. The stranger placed them in his hand one by one until he reached the tenth piece, which he hesitated over giving him.

'Come on! What are you waiting for?' asked Hoja. 'You promised me ten.'

Just then he awoke and immediately looking at his hand saw that it was empty. He quickly shut his eyes again, stretched out his hand and said, '

Alright! I'll settle for nine.'

The new moon

One day some friends tried to confuse Hoja by asking him, 'When there is a new moon, what do they do with the old one?'

Nasruddin, not wanting to show that he was ignorant about any subject, replied, 'They cut it up and it becomes stars.'

The trick

When Hoja lived in Sivrihisar, a proud young boy lived near him who was constantly boasting that no one could trick him.

'Wait here a while,' Hoja said to him one day, 'and I'll think of a way to trick you.'

Then Hoja walked away. Three hours later, the boy was still standing there. 'What are you waiting for?' asked a passer-by.

'I've been waiting for Hoja to find a way to trick me. I've been waiting here for three hours and he still hasn't returned.'

'Ha ha! Isn't it obvious that he has already tricked you by getting you to wait here all this time? How much longer are you going to stand there?'

Selling vegetables

Nasruddin Hoja decided to earn some money by buying vegetables wholesale and then selling them on the street. He strapped two large baskets on either side of the donkey, filled them to overflowing with vegetables and proceeded to walk through the town. Hoja wanted to get people's attention by shouting out 'vegetables', but every time he would open his mouth to do so the donkey would bray and no one could hear him.

So they arrived at the public square and Hoja shouted, 'Vegetables for sale!'

But at the same time the donkey brayed and drowned out his voice.

Hoja turned to the donkey and yelled, 'Now look here! Am I selling these vegetables, or are you?'

The wrong way

One day Nasruddin Hoja got on his donkey the wrong way, facing towards the back.

'Hoja,' people said, 'you are sitting on your donkey backwards!'

'No,' he replied, 'it's not that I'm sitting on my donkey backwards, but it is facing the wrong way.'

A good deal

It was market day and the grapes were being sold at a very low price. One of Hoja's friends urged him to go to the market and try to buy some at an even lower price.

So Nasruddin Hoja went to the market and began to bargain with the sellers. Finally, after much persuasion, he was able to buy the grapes at a very low price.

He returned to his friends and boasted, 'I did it! It wasn't easy but I succeeded. I had to haggle with the seller, plead with him and finally tell him all kinds of stories. In the end he believed my lies and agreed to give me the grapes very cheaply.'

'That's great,' replied his friend enthusiastically.

'It was because you insisted I did it,' Hoja said, 'but you must agree I deserve at least a little something for my labours.'

'Well of course,' replied the friend.

'Fine,' said Hoja, 'since I did all the work, I'll keep all the grapes for myself.'

34

I'm no fool

One day, Hoja went shopping in the market and bought many items so that his bag was full and heavy. It was too heavy for him to carry, so he gave it to a porter and followed behind him through the crowd. However, among all the people and confusion, he lost sight of the man and could not find him or his bag anywhere.

A week later, Hoja was walking through the same market with a friend when he saw the porter for whom he had been looking. Hoja immediately ran after him, but when he was right next to the porter he suddenly turned and hid. His friend who had followed him, asked, 'Hoja why are you hiding? You've been looking for this man all week and now that you've found him you're running away!'

'I'm no fool!' Hoja replied. 'If he sees me he will say that he has been carrying my bag around for seven days and I will have to pay him a fortune.

More light here

One day Hoja lost his ring inside the house somewhere. After looking for a while but not finding it, he went outside to look for it there. His neighbour asked him what he was looking for.

'I'm looking for my ring,' Nasruddin replied.

'Where did you lose it?' asked the neighbour.

'Somewhere in the house,' said Hoja.

'Then,' said the neighbour, 'why are you looking for it outside?'

'Because there is more light out here,' he answered.

Allah know's best

One hot summer day Hoja got off his donkey and lay down to rest under the shade of a walnut tree by a watermelon patch. He thought for a while and said, 'How strange is it of Allah that He created watermelons to grow on such tiny stalks while these little walnuts grow on such an immense tree.'

Just then a walnut fell from the tree and hit Hoja right on the head. Hoja rubbed his skull and said, 'Allah knows best! If watermelons grew on trees my head would have been seriously injured.'

I'm not the only one to blame

Once Hoja and his wife returned from an evening out and to their dismay they found that their house had been robbed!

'It's all your fault!' said his wife. 'You should have checked the house and made sure that it was locked before we left.'

All the neighbours agreed and started pointing their fingers at him too, saying:

'Why didn't you lock the windows?'

'What did you expect?'

'You were just asking for trouble.'

'Wait a minute,' interrupted Hoja, 'surely I'm not the only one to blame.'

'And who else should we blame?' they all shouted.

'Well,' he said, 'what about the thieves?'

Who is older?

When Hoja was a young boy an adult asked him, 'Who is older, you or your brother?'

Hoja stopped and thought for a minute and then answered, 'Well, last year my mother told me that my brother was one year older than me, so this year we must be the same age.'

Criticism

Hoja and his son went on a journey once. Hoja preferred that his son ride the donkey and that he would go on foot. On the way they met some people who said, 'Look at that healthy young boy! That's today's youth for you. They have no respect for their elders. He rides on the donkey and makes his poor father walk.'

When they had passed by these people, the boy felt very ashamed and insisted that he should walk and his father ride the donkey. So Hoja mounted the donkey and the boy walked at his side. A little later they met some other people who said, 'Well, look at that! That poor little boy has to walk while his father rides the donkey.'

After they had passed by these people, Hoja told his son, 'The best thing to do is for both of us to walk. Then no one can complain.'

So they continued on their journey, both of them walking. A little further down the road they met some other people who said, 'Just take a look at those fools. Both of them are walking under this hot sun and neither of them is riding the donkey.'

At this Hoja turned to his son and said, 'That just goes to show how hard it is to escape the opinions of men.'

Positive thinking

Once Hoja lost his donkey and he was searching every-where for it. While he was looking for it, he was con-stantly praising Allah. A passer-by asked him, 'I have heard that you lost your donkey. Why then are you praising Allah for this?'

'I thank Allah that I was not on it when it disappeared,' Hoja replied.

He continued looking for it, and then he change his praises to a merry song. Someone else asked, 'Why are you singing? When one loses one's donkey there is more cause for tears than for laughter.'

'Well,' he said, 'there's still hope that my donkey is on the other side of that hill over there.'

But hours passed and Hoja still hadn't found his don-key. So then he put up notices in the tea shops and public places which said that whoever found his don-key could keep it, and that Hoja would give him a sad-dle and bridle as well.

A friend asked, 'I just don't understand you. Why did you put up a notice like that? Now even if somebody finds the donkey it will no longer belong to you. What good is it to you?'

Hoja replied, 'Haven't you ever experienced the great pleasure that finding something gives you?'

An angry sultan

Sultan Timur was a very strict and powerful ruler and all of the people were afraid of him. One day he arrived in Aksehir with a very large army. Nasruddin Hoja did not like this 'invasion' of his home town and became very angry with the king.

He went up to him and asked him in an angry and threatening voice, 'Timur, are you and your army going to get out of this town or not?'

The Sultan was stunned by this statement and asked him what he meant.

Hoja shouted at the king, saying, 'Tell me if you are going to take your army and get out of here or not? If not I know what I'm going to do.'

This angered the Sultan even more and he roared back, 'If I don't leave what are you going to do about it?'

Hoja replied, 'I'll run away as fast as I can.'

Upside down

One day Hoja was talking to his friends and he said, 'When I die, I want you to bury me upside-down.'

'Why?' they asked in bewildered amazement.

'Because,' he said, 'I have heard that when the end of the world comes everything will be turned upside-down and so I will be the only one coming up the right way.'

The mercies of Allah

Late one night, Hoja looked out of his window and saw a large figure of a man with his arms stretched high above his head. He immediately woke his wife and said, 'Quick! Bring me my bow and arrows! There is some shady character in our garden.'

His wife ran and brought him what he wanted. Hoja drew back his bow and shot an arrow. It hit the apparition square in the belly.

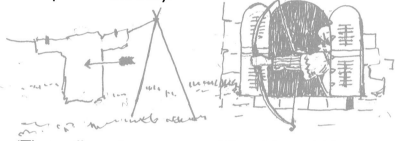

'That will teach you to meddle with me,' Hoja said proudly.

But none the less, he was afraid to go out into the garden and decided to wait until the morning. Next morning, he entered the garden and saw an arrow sticking out of his bath robe, which was hanging on the clothesline. Hoja fell on his knees and in a load voice began to give thanks to Allah.

'Why are you praying so earnestly?' inquired his wife.

'Can you not see, woman?' he answered. 'My arrow went right through the middle of my robe. If it hadn't been for the mercy of Allah I could have been wearing it at the time.'

A court-case

Hoja's friend stole some sacks of wheat and was caught by the officials. He had to go to court, so he asked Hoja to lie on his behalf.

When they questioned Hoja, be began to explain in a great deal of detail exactly what happened to those sacks of barley. The judge interrupted him by saying that he should be giving evidence concerning sacks of wheat, not barley. Nasruddin Hoja said to him, 'Sir, if one is lying, does it matter whether one lies about barley or wheat?'

The earth would tip over

One day someone asked Hoja, 'Why is it that as soon as it is day everyone gets up and goes in different directions?'

'Because,' Nasruddin Hoja replied, 'if everyone went off in the same direction the earth would tip over.'

Appearances

Once Hoja was invited to a very important formal banquet, but he didn't dress up for the occasion, rather he went in his everyday clothing. Once there, he was treated with disrespect and was looked upon with contempt. No one paid him any attention and the servants ignored him and didn't serve him dinner.

After a short while he slipped out of the banquet unnoticed and went home. There he changed into his finest clothes, putting on his magnificent turban, a fine silk robe, very valuable jewellery, and wore a large expensive fur coat over it all. Then he returned to the banquet.

This time he was received with open arms. The host himself bid him sit beside him at the highest seat and offered him a plate filled with the choicest delicacies. Much to their bewilderment, Hoja took off his coat, held it to the plate and said, 'Eat, my master, eat!'

'Hoja, what are you doing?' exclaimed his astonished host.

'It is the clothes that you are giving these delicacies to,' he said, 'not the man inside.'

One day…

One quiet Sunday afternoon Hoja was sitting at the crossroads. A friend came up to him and asked, 'Nasruddin, why are you sitting there? Nothing is happening.'

Hoja replied, 'But one day something will happen here, and a large crowd will gather. When that happens I might not be able to get close enough to see anything. So I'm putting my time in now.'

A practical joker

Once Hoja went on a long journey with a caravan. He was afraid he would get lost in the midst of so many people, so he decided to tie an eggplant to his belt so that he would be recognisable to all. One night, however, when they were all sleeping in the large tent, a practical joker removed the eggplant from his belt and tied it to his own. When Nasruddin awoke, he saw his eggplant on another man's belt. He was puzzled and said, 'That is me over there, but who am I here?'

Who told you?

One day Hoja was walking through the forest when he saw a large animal dart out of the bushes. This gave him

such a fright that he was sure that he had passed away. He lay on the ground for a long time, but no one came to carry his body away. Finally he got up and returned home where he told his wife just how he had died. Then he went over to the tea shop.

His wife was heartbroken over her husband's supposed death and began to cry loudly. She ran over to the neighbours and told them of the death of her poor husband. So they asked her, 'Where did he die?

'In the woods outside of town,' she replied.

'Who told you?' they asked.

'Oh, that's the sad thing about it,' she explained, 'he died all alone and there was no one to carry him home, so the poor man had to walk all the way back to tell me himself.'

Lute lessons

Hoja always wanted to learn something new, so one day he had a sudden inspiration to learn how to play the lute.

He approached a music teacher and asked him, 'How much do you charge for private lute lessons?'

'Three silver pieces for the first month,' he answered, 'then after that one silver piece a month.

'O, great!' exclaimed Hoja. 'Then I'll start the second month.'

I'll carry it

Hoja went to the market and bought a large sack full of potatoes. He put the sack on his shoulders, got on to the donkey and headed for home. But on the way he met some friends who said, 'Hoja, it must be difficult for you to balance that sack with one hand and guide the donkey with the other. Why don't you tie the sack to the donkey?'

'The donkey has a big enough load to carry with me,' he answered, 'and doesn't need any extra weight so I'll carry the sack myself.'

The sultan's visit

The sultan was going to visit Hoja's town but Nasruddin Hoja wasn't sure how he should behave in the presence of the king. One of the king's officials briefed him how he should answer the king's standard questions. The official said that the sultan would ask him how long he had been living there and how many years he had studied. So Hoja memorised his answers, but the king asked them in another order.

He asked, 'How many years have you studied?'

'Thirty-eight years, your majesty,' said Hoja.

'Then how old are you?' the sultan asked.

'Thirteen years old, your majesty,' said Nasruddin.

'What?' exclaimed the sultan. 'How can that be? Are you crazy, or am I?'

'Both of us are, your highness,' said Nasruddin, 'but in different ways.'

A left-handed horse

Hoja was preparing to travel. When a horse was brought to him he put his right foot in the left stirrup and pulled himself up on the horse. There he found himself sitting backwards with the horse's head behind him.

'Hey there!' cried Hoja angrily. 'You have given me a left-handed horse.'

Don't ask me

Hoja was riding on his donkey one day when something in it's path frightened it and it began to run very fast. He was not able to hold his donkey back.

Some farmers yelled at him, 'Hoja, what's the hurry? Why are you going so fast?'

'Don't ask me,' he shouted back, 'ask the donkey.'

She feels better

Once Hoja's wife was very sick and she asked him to call the doctor. Nasruddin Hoja was very worried about his wife's condition so he hurried out the door. As he passed by the window, however, his wife stuck her head out the window and shouted, 'Praise be to Allah! The pain has ceased and I no longer need a doctor.'

Hoja heard her and ran to the doctor's house and said, 'Doctor, my wife was very ill and she asked me to call you. But as I was leaving she told me that she suddenly felt better and that she no longer needed a doctor. I came to tell you not to come.'

The gold coin

Hoja was sitting in a tea house when a stranger came in and asked him, 'Hoja, can you change this gold coin into small silver coins for me?'

Hoja didn't have any silver coins at all, nor any money of any kind with which to change it but he didn't want to admit this in front of his friends. So he took the gold piece and held it thoughtfully in his hand and said, 'This coin is underweight. I cannot change it for you at it's face value.'

'Then just give me what you think it is worth,' replied the man.

'But it is very, very much underweight,' insisted Hoja.

'Oh no, what a shame!' replied the man. 'But I need the change and I'd really appreciate it if you could give me whatever little you think it's worth.'

Hoja, seeing that this man was not going to give up and not wanting to lose face before his friends, said to him, 'This coin is so underweight that if I change it, you will owe me money.'

A thief

One night a thief broke into Hoja's house.

'Honey,' whispered his wife, 'there's a thief in the next room.'

'Shhh!' he whispered back. 'Perhaps he will find something worth stealing, and then we can easily take it away from him.'

He is out

Nasruddin Hoja went to a castle once to ask for money as charity.

'Tell your master,' he said to the doorkeeper, 'that Hoja is here and that he is asking for money.'

The doorkeeper went inside the castle for a while and then came out and said, 'I'm afraid that my master is out.'

'Oh, is that so?' said Hoja. 'Then give him a message from me, that even though he has not contributed anything, he can have this advice for free! Next time he goes out, tell him that he shouldn't leave his face looking out the window, somebody might steal it.'

It might be true

One day Hoja was walking down the village street when some boys started to throw stones at him. He looked at them and said, 'If you stop throwing stones at me, I'll tell you something that will interest you.'

All the boys put down their stones and said, 'Alright then, tell us.'

'The mayor is giving a free banquet and you are all invited,' improvised Hoja.

The children were delighted to hear this news and all of them ran off towards the mayor's house.

Hoja was pleased with his quick thinking but then he said to himself, 'I'd better go there and see for myself, after all, it might be true.'

A mirror's reflection

Nasruddin Hoja was walking down the street when he noticed something glittering in the gutter. He ran over to pick it up and saw that it was a small metal mirror. He looked in it and said to himself, 'No wonder they threw this away! I wouldn't keep something so ugly either.'

Foretelling the future

Once Hoja was sitting in a tree cutting wood. A passer-by saw that Hoja was sawing away at the branch on which he was sitting right there in between himself and the tree.

The man looked up and said, 'You and that branch will fall down if you continue sawing it that way.'

Hoja didn't pay any attention and kept on sawing.

Suddenly the branch creaked, broke off and Hoja

fell heavily to the ground. He pulled himself to his feet and ran limping after the man, as fast as he could. Catching up to him he said, 'Sir, I perceive that you have the gift of being able to foretell the future. If you knew that I would fall from that tree, surely you must know when I will die.'

The stranger saw at once that he couldn't explain anything to him, so he cut matters short by saying, 'When your donkey brays once, half of your soul will leave your body and when it brays a second time, you will die.'

Hoja was very shocked and worried when he heard this. He went to his donkey, loaded it with firewood and headed for home. On the way his donkey brayed. He grew pale and felt very ill. A little later when the donkey brayed a second time, Hoja fell to the ground and shouted, 'I am dead!'

He laid there with his eyes closed. A little later a group of villagers saw him there. Hoja looked so pale that they all thought he was dead. They got a large long wooden box, placed him in it and proceeded to carry him down the road. When they came to a fork in the road, they couldn't decide which road to take so they began to argue.

Hoja, already much bothered by all the jostling in his uncomfortable box, couldn't take it any more. He lifted up his head and said, 'When I was alive I took the road to the left.'

All things are possible

One day Hoja's neighbour came to his house to have a chat with him. Hoja didn't want to talk to him so he told his wife to say that he wasn't home. The neighbour said, 'But I saw Hoja entering the house just a little while ago.'

Hoja was sitting by the window listening to him. When he understood that the man didn't believe his wife, he got very angry and opened the window and shouted, 'You foolish man! Doesn't this house have both a front door and a back door? Isn't it possible that I could have gone out the back door?'

Guess

One of the village boys came up to Hoja and asked, 'Are you any good at guessing games?'

'Of course I am,' replied Hoja.

'All right then,' said the boy, 'what do I have in my pocket?'

'Give me a hint,' said Hoja.

'It is round like an egg, white and yellow inside,' the boy said, 'and it looks like an egg.'

'A piece of banana?' Hoja guessed.

The Hoja's handwriting

Hoja Nasruddin was very well educated. He had gone to the finest schools in the city. One day a poor illiterate farmer approached him and requested him to write a letter for him.

'Where will you send this letter?' asked Hoja.

'To Baghdad,' replied the farmer.

'But I cannot go there!' Hoja complained.

'But you don't need to go there,' the farmer said. 'I just want you to send this letter there.'

Hoja then explained, 'You see, nobody can read my handwriting, so I would have to go there and read the letter to them myself.'

A bright idea

At one time in his life, Hoja was living in a house with another person. Then he had the bright idea to sell half of the house. So he called the real-estate agent.

The agent remarked, 'This is the wrong time of the year to sell. And why do you only want to sell half the house?'

Hoja replied, 'I don't like sharing the house with anybody. I must sell my half to get the money to buy the other half.'

His will

The time came for Hoja Nasruddin to write his own will. He simply wrote, 'I have nothing. Let this be divided according to the shari'ah between each member of my immediate family. That which is left over should be given to the poor.'

The end of the world

One day someone asked Hoja, 'Hoja, when will the end of the world come?'

'Which end of the world?' Nasruddin asked.

'What do you mean?' the man asked in utter bewilderment. 'How many ends of the world are there?'

'Two,' said Hoja. 'The first will be when my wife dies. The second when I die.'